The Cemetery Dance

Level 5G

Written by Lucy George
Illustrated by Ayesha Lopez Rubio

What is synthetic phonics?

Synthetic phonics teaches children to recognise the sounds of letters and to blend (synthesise) them together to make whole words.

Understanding sound/letter relationships gives children the confidence and ability to read unfamiliar words, without having to rely on memory or guesswork; this helps them to progress towards independent reading.

Did you know? Spoken English uses more than 40 speech sounds. Each sound is called a *phoneme*. Some phonemes relate to a single letter (d-o-g) and others to combinations of letters (sh-ar-p). When a phoneme is written down it is called a *grapheme*. Teaching these sounds, matching them to their written form and sounding out words for reading is the basis of synthetic phonics.

Consultant

I love reading phonics has been created in consultation with language expert Abigail Steel. She has a background in teaching and teacher training and is a respected expert in the field of synthetic phonics. Abigail Steel is a regular contributor to educational publications. Her international education consultancy supports parents and teachers in the promotion of literacy skills.

Reading tips

This book focuses on the s sound, made with the letters ce, as in prince.

Tricky words in this book

Any words in bold may have unusual spellings or are new and have not yet been introduced.

> ### Tricky words in this book:
>
> ## know once creatures yourself zombies ghouls ghosts witches friends

Extra ways to have fun with this book

After the reader has read the story, ask them questions about what they have just read:

Who went to the cemetery dance?

Can you remember three words that contain the s sound made with the letters ce?

You'll have the night of your life! Did I say night? I meant fright...

A pronunciation guide

This grid contains the sounds used in the stories in levels 4, 5 and 6 and a guide on how to say them. /a/ represents the sounds made, rather than the letters in a word.

/ai/ as in game	/ai/ as in play/they	/ee/ as in leaf/these	/ee/ as in he
/igh/ as in kite/light	/igh/ as in find/sky	/oa/ as in home	/oa/ as in snow
/oa/ as in cold	/y+oo/ as in cube/music/new	long /oo/ as in flute/crew/blue	/oi/ as in boy
/er/ as in bird/hurt	/or/ as in snore/oar/door	/or/ as in dawn/sauce/walk	/e/ as in head
/e/ as in said/any	/ou/ as in cow	/u/ as in touch	/air/ as in hare/bear/there
/eer/ as in deer/here/cashier	/t/ as in tripped/skipped	/d/ as in rained	/j/ as in gent/gin/gym
/j/ as in barge/hedge	/s/ as in cent/circus/cyst	/s/ as in prince	/s/ as in house
/ch/ as in itch/catch	/w/ as in white	/h/ as in who	/r/ as in write/rhino

Sounds this story focuses on
are highlighted in the grid.

/**f**/ as in phone	/**f**/ as in rough	/**ul**/ as in pencil/ hospital	/**z**/ as in fries/ cheese/breeze
/**n**/ as in knot/ gnome/engine	/**m**/ as in welcome /thumb/column	/**g**/ as in guitar/ghost	/**zh**/ as in vision/beige
/**k**/ as in chord	/**k**/ as in plaque/ bouquet	/**nk**/ as in uncle	/**ks**/ as in box/books/ ducks/cakes
/**a**/ and /**o**/ as in hat/what	/**e**/ and /**ee**/ as in bed/he	/**i**/ and /**igh**/ as in fin/find	/**o**/ and /**oa**/ as in hot/cold
/**u**/ and short /**oo**/ as in but/put	/**ee**/, /**e**/ and /**ai**/ as in eat/ bread/break	/**igh**/, /**ee**/ and /**e**/ as in tie/field/friend	/**ou**/ and /**oa**/ as in cow/blow
/**ou**/, /**oa**/ and /**oo**/ as in out/ shoulder/could	/**i**/ and /**ai**/ as in money/they	/**c**/ and /**s**/ as in cat/cent	/**y**/, /**igh**/ and /**i**/ as in yes/sky/myth
/**g**/ and /**j**/ as in got/giant	/**ch**/, /**c**/ and /**sh**/ as in chin/ school/chef	/**er**/, /**air**/ and /**eer**/ as in earth/bear/ears	/**u**/, /**ou**/ and /**oa**/ as in plough/dough

Be careful not to add an 'uh' sound to 's', 't', 'p',
'c', 'h', 'r', 'm', 'd', 'g', 'l', 'f' and 'b'. For example,
say 'fff' not 'fuh' and 'sss' not 'suh'.

Did you **know**, that
once a century, on the
night of Halloween...

ever since time began,
something happens right
here in this cemetery...

When the moon glances off
gravestones, and the wind
blows in the trees,

the deceased rise up, and
creatures of the night join
them for... brace **yourself**...

A dance! That's right, a dance!
It's the cemetery dance of the
century!

Creatures of the night gather
every hundredth Halloween for
this party!

Zombies pounce and drink juice from poisoned chalices.

Ghouls wail with forced, loud voices.

Centaurs prance and bounce
with grace.

Ghosts flounce in their best lace dresses.

Vampires grimace and act like menaces.

Witches embrace and entice old **friends** to join in...

...and they all dance together!

They dance, prance, flounce
and bounce.

And do you know what?

They don't cease until the
sun comes up... they dance all
night long.

But when it's all over,
they make themselves scarce;
they don't leave a trace.

But take my advice, don't go
looking, because you might not
be able to handle the pace!

OVER 48 TITLES IN SIX LEVELS
Abigail Steel recommends...

Some titles from Level 4

978-1-84898-582-7   978-1-84898-583-4   978-1-84898-585-8

Other titles to enjoy from Level 5

978-1-84898-586-5   978-1-84898-587-2   978-1-84898-589-6

Some titles from Level 6

978-1-84898-590-2   978-1-84898-591-9   978-1-84898-592-6

An Hachette UK Company
www.hachette.co.uk

Copyright © Octopus Publishing Group Ltd 2012
First published in Great Britain in 2012 by TickTock, an imprint of Octopus Publishing Group Ltd,
Endeavour House, 189 Shaftesbury Avenue, London WC2H 8JY.
www.octopusbooks.co.uk

ISBN 978 1 84898 588 9

Printed and bound in China
10 9 8 7 6 5 4 3 2 1